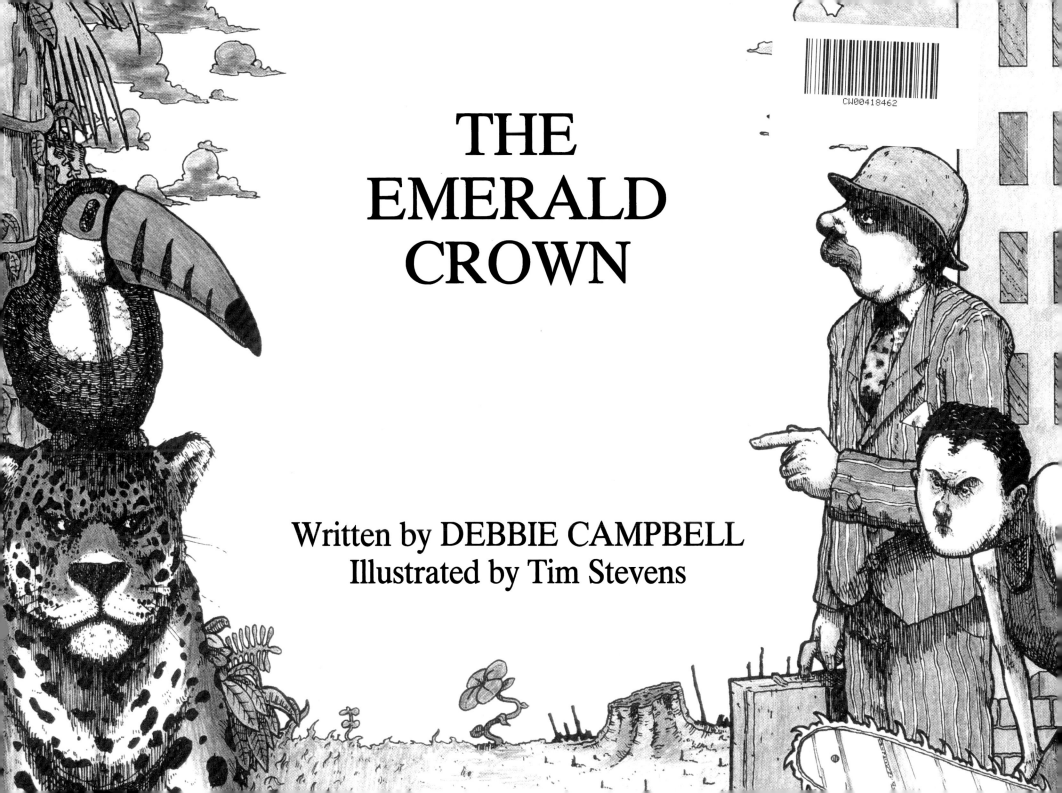

# THE EMERALD CROWN

Written by DEBBIE CAMPBELL
Illustrated by Tim Stevens

As part of the international WWF network, WWF-UK addresses threats to people and nature such as climate change, pollution, and the unsustainable consumption of the world's natural resources.

WWF's education programme was established in the early 1980s, encouraging schools to put sustainability at the heart of school life. WWF's new One Planet Schools programme provides schools with a range of engaging and inspiring activities which show how all schools can play a part in striving to live within the ecological limits of one planet.

WWF has a rich history of producing musicals for primary schools, in collaboration with Debbie Campbell. Schools right across the UK and internationally have performed this unique range of engaging and fun musicals, which have a serious and important message about the health and welfare of the planet on which we all depend.

More information about WWF's One Planet Schools programme can be found at:
**www.wwf.org.uk/oneplanetschools**

# THE EMERALD CROWN

At a busy airport somewhere near the Amazon Rainforest, a plane landed. Among its passengers was a smartly-dressed but aggressive businessman, carrying a briefcase. He quickly left for an important meeting.

>Twentieth-century highwayman
>Travels the world and he takes what he can.
>He's a jet-setting, go-getting twentieth-century man.
>He lives in a city far away —
>An urban jungle of concrete and clay
>In a jet-setting, go-getting twentieth-century land.

Chorus
>*Stand and deliver!*
>*He's heading for the Amazon River.*
>*He'll rob from the forest and steal from the trees.*
>*He gets what he wants —*
>*And he wants what he sees.*

>Twentieth-century highwayman
>Travels the world and he takes what he can.
>He's a jet-setting, go-getting twentieth-century man.
>He's looking for treasure to steal away
>And take to the city of concrete and clay
>In a jet-setting, go-getting twentieth-century land.
>*Stand and deliver!*
>*He's heading for the Amazon River.*
>*He'll rob from the forest and steal from the trees.*
>*He gets what he wants —*
>*And he wants what he sees.*

In the middle of a beautiful rainforest, Twentieth-Century Highwayman was making a deal with a gang of tough-looking workers. He offered them money from his briefcase to destroy the surrounding trees. They were poor and so they accepted, and began to slash and burn the trees. A horrified toucan observed from above.

>I was chatting away quite happily
>With my feathered friends in the family tree;
>Flapping and rapping in the steaming heat
>To the funky rhythm of the jungle beat.

When suddenly I heard the sound
Of timber crashing to the ground,
And all around was smoke and fire
Climbing upwards higher and higher.

So down I went to investigate
The reason for this dreadful state
And to my surprise what I did see
Was a gang of guys vandalising my tree.

And as the workmen cut down the trees, they sang to
the rhythm of their work.

We slash and burn to earn our pay;
Slash and burn, slash and burn.
The roar of the saw goes on all day;
Slash and burn, slash and burn.
Our work has only just begun,
There's plenty here for everyone,
And when it's gone we'll just move on.

And when we've cleared the trees away,
Slash and burn, slash and burn,
We'll drive the herds to earn our pay;
Slash and burn, slash and burn.
Our work has only just begun,
There's plenty here for everyone,
And when it's gone we'll just move on.

And when the herds no longer pay,
Slash and burn, slash and burn,
We're gonna make a great highway;
Slash and burn, slash and burn.
Our work has only just begun,
There's plenty here for everyone,
And when it's gone we'll just move on.

And when we've made the great highway,
Slash and burn, slash and burn,
We'll pack our bags and drive away;
Slash and burn, slash and burn.
Our work has only just begun,
There's plenty here for everyone,
And when it's gone we'll just move on.


I said 'What do you think you're doing
Causing all this rack and ruin?'
And they replied 'We're on a mission —
These trees are due for demolition.

Now, bird-brain if you know what's best
You'll find yourself another nest,
But if you dare to stick around
You'll end up there down on the ground.'

I cried 'Do any of you know
How long it took my tree to grow?
A bird-brained toucan I may be
But at least I know how to treat a tree!'


It takes a hundred years for a forest tree to grow.
A giant in the sky, climbing way up high,
Growing in the earth below.
But by the time I've sung my song
A thousand trees like these will be gone.
How long will it be before you can see
That what you are doing is wrong?

It takes ten thousand years for a forest tribe to
  know
The secrets of the flowers, their magic healing
  powers,
Growing in the earth below.
But by the time I've sung my song
A thousand flowers like these will be gone.
How long will it be before you can see
That what you are doing is wrong?

It takes a hundred million years for a forest to grow.
A canopy of green, the greatest ever seen,
Sheltering the earth below.
But now it won't be very long
Till forests of the earth will be gone.
How long will it be before you can see
That what you are doing is wrong?

Then I flew off to the river yonder
Where I knew a great big anaconda.
She greeted me and hugged and squeezed me
Like she was really pleased to see me.

I said 'Now's not the time for that.
Our forest's under an attack.'
She said 'My faith is in you Toucan.
If anyone can save it, you can.'

It was time to educate these guys
And try and make them realise.
I'd take them on a guided tour
And show them sights never seen before.

I said 'If you stop that chopping down
I'll lead you to the Emerald Crown
And take you where no human's been,
And there we'll meet the Jungle Queen.'

Although they tried they could not disguise
The greedy look that was in their eyes.
They thought they'd go along with me
Then steal all the jewellery.

And so they began their journey, with the Toucan and Anaconda leading the workers deeper and deeper into the forest.

We travelled for a hundred days
Unravelling the jungle maze
A paradise of epiphytes
And brightly-painted parasites.

Down on the ground where the sun doesn't shine,
Twisty and tangly creepers entwine.
Leaves flutter by and then settle to lie
Down on the ground where the sun doesn't shine.

Down on the ground where it rains every day,
Misty, mysterious, gloomy and grey.
Creatures come creeping then scurry away
Down on the ground where it rains every day.

Down on the ground... Down on the ground.

But right up high and where the forest meets the
    sky
Is a bright evergreen with the most exotic sights
    you have ever seen —
Colours that will dazzle your eyes, sounds that will
    surprise.

We gorged on fruits that grew around
And roots we found under the ground.
Avocados and bananas,
Mangoes, pineapples and guavas.

We paddled in the Amazon
Where fishes flashed and darted on,
Piranhas and electric eels
Searching for their tasty meals.

We met some fierce inhabitants
Like poisonous frogs and army ants;
And sometimes we would stop for chats
With colonies of barmy bats.

Laze about, hanging round,
Inside out, upside down.
Ain't we just the strangest things?
Sleepy-heads in the air,
Got no beds but we don't care,
Furry things with shiny wings.

But then the bats suddenly woke up and began quickly flapping their wings.

We're bats, we're bats, we're absolutely bats!
We hang about and sleep all day,
At night time we go out to play,
We spread our wings and fly away,
We're absolutely bats!

We're bats, we're bats, we're absolutely bats!
We live in caves and roofs and trees,
We live on bugs and flies and fleas,
We do exactly as we please,
We're absolutely bats!

We're bats, we're bats, we're absolutely bats!
With beady eyes and turned-up snouts
And toothy grin our ears stick out,
We squeak to help us get about,
We're absolutely bats!

And every day it rained and rained
And often we were entertained
By howler monkeys crying out
To other monkeys round about.

A two-toed sloth cried 'Here below
We're trying to sleep so keep the sound
Down low, low, low,
At the jungle disco.'
But the monkeys they were unaware
Or else they simply didn't care
To know, know, know
At the jungle disco.

Howling, hollering, growling, quarrelling,
Thumping, clattering, jumping, chattering,
Oh no, no,
It's the jungle disco.

Every day when the tree tops sway
The monkeys say 'It's time to play,
Let's go, go, go
To the jungle disco.'
And all the swingers from around
Start howling to the jungle sound,
They go 'Oh, oh, oh,
It's the jungle disco'.

An angry snake from the basement said
'The noise they make will wake the dead.
They'll have to go
At the jungle disco.'
And a poor macaw from the tree next door
    squawked
'I can't stand it any more
Oh no, no, no,
It's the jungle disco.'

One night we heard a mighty roar
And saw the footprint of a paw.
And then we spied Her Majesty
Reclining high up in a tree.

The Queen of the Jungle emerged slowly from her
hiding place.

Amazon cat goes out at night,
Wild cat, wild cat,
Dressed to kill and out of sight,
Wild cat, wild cat,
High upon her leafy throne she waits alone.

*Chorus*     *Wild cat, wild cat,*
*Queen of the jungle that's what you are —*
*Jaguar.*
*Wild cat, wild cat,*
*Amazon aristocrat.*

Dreaming of what her prey may be,
Wild cat, wild cat,
Capybara, Peccary,
Wild cat, wild cat,
Or a poor monkey fallen from a tree.
*Wild cat, wild cat,*
*Queen of the jungle that's what you are —*
*Jaguar.*
*Wild cat, wild cat,*
*Amazon aristocrat.*

Then one man sneered 'Whatever's that?
It's just a great big pussycat.
She's not much like a queen to me,
And where is all her jewellery?

This treasure isn't worth a dime,
You've just wasted our precious time,
So come on guys without delay
Let's clear the lot of it away.'

But when they started to attack
The jaguar bravely held them back
While I relayed an S.O.S.
For help to get us out this mess.

The forest creatures heard the call,
And they responded one and all,
And swiftly came from near and far
To stand beside the Jaguar.

And then she walked up to the guys
And glared at them with golden eyes,
And said 'Oh men of little brain
Don't ever kill our trees again.

For money doesn't grow on trees,
But precious treasures such as these
And they cannot be bought and sold
With sterling currency and gold.'

You've seen and heard my bird's-eye view,
Now you can help a toucan too.
Just put a stop to all this wrong
And start by joining in my song.

There is an emerald crown in every tree top...

There is a shimmering pearl in every raindrop...

There is a hummingbird that glitters like a jewel in the
    crown...

There is a butterfly that flitters in a sapphire gown...

There is a jaguar blinking with a golden eye...

There is a crystal star twinkling in a jet-black sky...

Look around, look around,
Look around and see what you have found.
Search no more, search no more,
Search no more, this is what you came here for.
For every tree, every creature that you see
Is a treasure in its own special way, so I say

Let it stay, let it stay,
Let it stay, you can't take it away.
Let it stay, let it stay,
Let it stay.

And all the slashers and burners, cattle-herders and road constructors, joined in together with the creatures and sang.

It takes a hundred years for a forest tree to grow.
A giant in the sky, climbing way up high,
Growing in the earth below.
But by the time I've sung my song
A thousand trees like these will be gone.
How long will it be before we can see
That what we are doing is wrong?

It takes ten thousand years for a forest tribe to
    know
The secrets of the flowers, their magic healing
    powers,
Growing in the earth below.
But by the time I've sung my song
A thousand flowers like these will be gone.
How long will it be before we can see
That what we are doing is wrong?

It takes a hundred million years for a forest to grow.
A canopy of green, the greatest ever seen,
Sheltering the earth below.
But now it won't be very long
Till forests of the earth will be gone.
How long will it be before we can see
That what we are doing is wrong?

# OVERTURE

*Play this if leading straight into 'Twentieth-century highwayman'.

# TWENTIETH-CENTURY HIGHWAYMAN

(Instruments - hard percussive drum, cymbal, wood block)

1. Twen-ti-eth-cen-tu-ry high-way-man_____ Tra-vels the world and he takes what he can. He's a
lives in a ci-ty far a-way— An ur-ban jun-gle of con-crete and clay In a
2. Twen-ti-eth-cen-tu-ry high-way-man_____ Tra-vels the world and he takes what he can. He's a
look-ing for trea-sure to steal a-way And take to the ci-ty of con-crete and clay In a

jet-set-ting, go-get-ting twen-ti-eth-cen-tu-ry man._____ He
jet-set-ting, go-get-ting twen-ti-eth-cen-tu-ry land._____
jet-set-ting, go-get-ting twen-ti-eth-cen-tu-ry - man._____ He's
jet-set-ting, go-get-ting twen-ti-eth-cen-tu-ry land._____

*Or you can play a downward chromatic scale over two octaves in these four bars, starting an octave higher.

NOTE: During this song the Highwayman walks away from the plane toward the rainforest. In the chorus he/she imitates a hold-up.

CHORUS

Stand and de - li - ver! He's head-ing for the A - ma - zon Ri - ver. He'll rob from the fo - rest and steal from the trees. He gets what he wants— And he wants what he

I was chatting away quite happily
With my feathered friends in the family tree;
Flapping and rapping in the steaming heat
To the funky rhythm of the jungle beat.

When suddenly I heard the sound
Of timber crashing to the ground,
And all around was smoke and fire
Climbing upwards higher and higher.

So down I went to investigate
The reason for this dreadful state
And to my surprise what I did see
Was a gang of guys vandalising my tree.

# SLASH AND BURN

(Instruments - Bass Drum, rasp, woodblock)

NOTE: v.1 is sung by slashers and burners, v.2 by cattle-herders, v.3 by road constructors, v.4 by all the workers.
At the end of their verse each group turns and walks away with a nonchalant shrug.

I said 'What do you think you're doing
Causing all this rack and ruin?'
And they replied 'We're on a mission —
These trees are due for demolition.

Now, bird-brain if you know what's best
You'll find yourself another nest,
But if you dare to stick around
You'll end up there down on the ground.'

I cried 'Do any of you know
How long it took my tree to grow?
A bird-brained toucan I may be
But at least I know how to treat a tree!'

# IT TAKES A HUNDRED YEARS

**Flowing** ♩=100

1. It takes a hun‑dred years for a
2. It takes ten thou‑sand years for a
3. It takes a hun‑dred mil‑lion

NOTE: v.1 is sung by the Toucan, v.2 by the Toucan and other birds, v.3 by all the creatures.

A thou-sand trees like these will be gone. How
A thou-sand flowers like these will be gone.
Till fo-rests of the earth will be gone.

long will it be be-fore you can see* That what you are do-ing is wrong? How

long will it be be-fore you can see That what you are do-ing is wrong?

*When sung by animals. When sung by human characters or audience, sing 'we'.

Then I flew off to the river yonder
Where I knew a great big anaconda.
She greeted me and hugged and squeezed me
Like she was really pleased to see me.

I said 'Now's not the time for that.
Our forest's under an attack.'
She said 'My faith is in you Toucan.
If anyone can save it, you can.'

It was time to educate these guys
And try and make them realise.
I'd take them on a guided tour
And show them sights never seen before.

I said 'If you stop that chopping down
I'll lead you to the Emerald Crown
And take you where no human's been,
And there we'll meet the Jungle Queen.'

Although they tried they could not disguise
The greedy look that was in their eyes.
They thought they'd go along with me
Then steal all the jewellery.

We travelled for a hundred days
Unravelling the jungle maze
A paradise of epiphytes
And brightly-painted parasites.

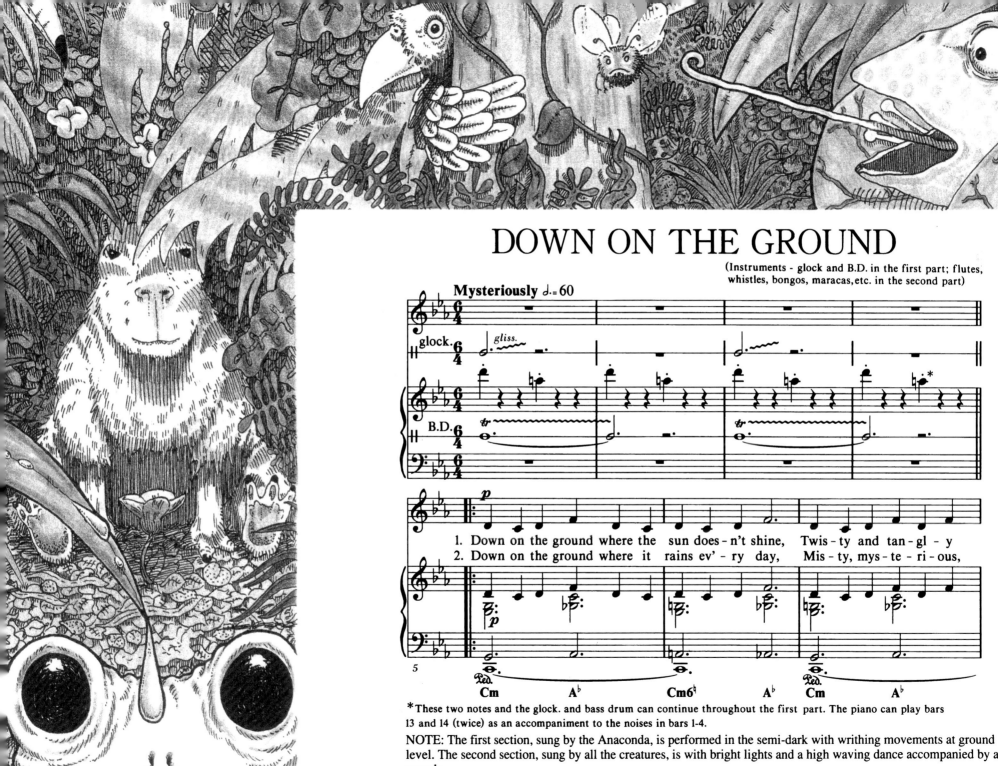

# DOWN ON THE GROUND

(Instruments - glock and B.D. in the first part; flutes, whistles, bongos, maracas, etc. in the second part)

**Mysteriously** ♩.= 60

glock.

B.D.

1. Down on the ground where the sun does-n't shine, Twis-ty and tan-gl-y
2. Down on the ground where it rains ev'-ry day, Mis-ty, mys-te-ri-ous,

Cm   A♭   Cm6♮   A♭   Cm   A♭

*These two notes and the glock. and bass drum can continue throughout the first part. The piano can play bars 13 and 14 (twice) as an accompaniment to the noises in bars 1-4.

NOTE: The first section, sung by the Anaconda, is performed in the semi-dark with writhing movements at ground level. The second section, sung by all the creatures, is with bright lights and a high waving dance accompanied by animal sounds.

creep - ers en - twine.   Leaves flut - ter by and then set - tle to lie  Down on the ground where the ' sun does - n't shine.
gloom - y and grey.   Crea - tures come creep - ing then scur - ry a - way  Down on the ground where it rains ev' - ry day.

Cm6   A♭  Fm     D♭  Fm6   D♭  Cm5♭  E♭7   Dm7  G5♯

Down _____ on the ground. _____  Down _____ on the

Cm  A♭  Cm6  A♭   Cm  A♭  Cm6  A♭   Cm  A♭  Cm6  A♭

**Brightly** ♩=132 *bossanova rhythm*

ground. _____ But right up high _  and where the fo - rest meets the sky _____  Is a

Cm A♭ Cm6 A♭  Fmaj7           E♭maj7

*These four bars of 'sounds' can be repeated, second time around.

We gorged on fruits that grew around
And roots we found under the ground.
Avocados and bananas,
Mangoes, pineapples and guavas.

We paddled in the Amazon
Where fishes flashed and darted on,
Piranhas and electric eels
Searching for their tasty meals.

We met some fierce inhabitants
Like poisonous frogs and army ants;
And sometimes we would stop for chats
With colonies of barmy bats.

# WE'RE BATS

And every day it rained and rained
And often we were entertained
By howler monkeys crying out
To other monkeys round about.

# JUNGLE DISCO

(Instruments - synthesizer, cymbals, maracas, woodblock, cowbell)

NOTE: The monkeys spring out from the trees, and perform a lively dance.

One night we heard a mighty roar
And saw the footprint of a paw.
And then we spied Her Majesty
Reclining high up in a tree.

# WILD CAT

(Instruments - drums and cymbals, with brushes; cello or bass pizzicato)

**Mysteriously** ♩= 112

growl or hiss

Cymbal

cymbal etc. ad lib.

R.H.

A7

A7

A7

1. A - ma - zon cat___ goes out at___ night,___ Wild cat, wild cat,
2. Dream-ing of what___ her prey may___ be,___ Wild cat, wild cat,

Dm     Dm7     B♭7     A7     Gm7     F     E7     A7

NOTE: The Jaguar emerges stealthily, and dances with prowling movements.

Then one man sneered 'Whatever's that?
It's just a great big pussycat.
She's not much like a queen to me,
And where is all her jewellery?

This treasure isn't worth a dime,
You've just wasted our precious time,
So come on guys without delay
Let's clear the lot of it away.'

But when they started to attack
The jaguar bravely held them back
While I relayed an S.O.S.
For help to get us out this mess.

The forest creatures heard the call,
And they responded one and all,
And swiftly came from near and far
To stand beside the Jaguar.

And then she walked up to the guys
And glared at them with golden eyes,
And said 'Oh men of little brain
Don't ever kill our trees again.

For money doesn't grow on trees,
But precious treasures such as these
And they cannot be bought and sold
With sterling currency and gold.'

NOTE: The 'S.O.S.' can be the melody of 'There is an Emerald Crown' (p.42).

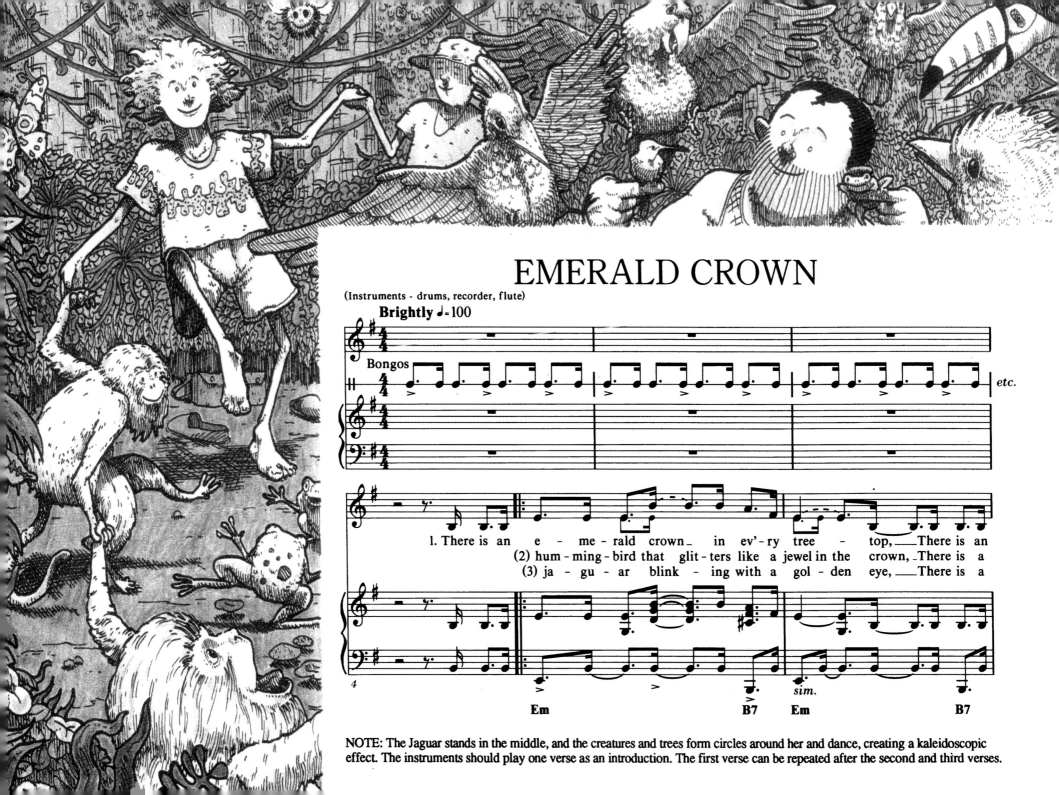

# EMERALD CROWN

(Instruments - drums, recorder, flute)

**Brightly** ♩=100

Bongos

*etc.*

1. There is an e - me - rald crown in ev'-ry tree - top, There is an
(2) hum - ming - bird that glit - ters like a jewel in the crown, There is a
(3) ja - gu - ar blink - ing with a gol - den eye, There is a

Em   B7   Em   B7

NOTE: The Jaguar stands in the middle, and the creatures and trees form circles around her and dance, creating a kaleidoscopic effect. The instruments should play one verse as an introduction. The first verse can be repeated after the second and third verses.

# LOOK AROUND

(Instruments - drums, recorder, flute)

Flowing ♩=100

Look a - round, _____ look a -
more, _____ Search no

*Start at bar 2 when carrying straight on from 'Emerald Crown'

You've seen and heard my bird's-eye view,
Now you can help a toucan too.
Just put a stop to all this wrong
And start by joining in my song.

NOTE: After the final rap from the Toucan, all the characters and audience sing 'It takes a hundred years' (p. 23).